A hen has six little
chickens on the grass.

'Cheep, cheep,' say
the six little chickens.
'Cheep, cheep.'

Kevin runs on the grass. The six little chickens run away.

Oh no! The hen has lost the six little chickens.

She goes to look for
the chickens in the
shed. No chickens!

She goes to look for
the chickens in the
hut. No chickens!

She goes to look for
the chickens in the
kennel.

All the chickens are on Wellington. Cheep, cheep, cheep!